The Aztecs

Five hundred years ago the Aztecs were the most powerful people in their part of the world. Although most people know them as Aztecs, they called themselves Mexica. Does that give you a clue to the modern name of their country?

M _ _ _ _ _ _

Many other groups of people also lived in the area, speaking many different languages. Some of them were allies and others traded with the Aztec, like the Maya in the south. Some, like the Tlaxcallans, were their enemies. Some people think there were about twenty million people in Mexico in around 1500 AD. One hundred years later, there were only about one to two million native people left. This was because of new diseases, war and slavery brought to the country by Europeans after the Spanish Conquest.

Can you find Mexico in an atlas? Find the two main mountain ranges and put them on this map. Can you see which areas are desert and which are rain forest? Mark those on this map too.

HUASTECS

CHICHIMECS

Tochpan

Lake Texcoco

Tenochtitlan

TARASCANS

TLAXCALLANS

Gulf of Mexico

MAYA

Chiapan

Monte Albán

Acapulco

MIXTECS

Pacific Ocean

Mazatlan

D1534437

United States

Mexico

When did the Aztecs live?

The Aztecs lived in the Valley of Mexico for over 200 years before the Spaniards conquered them in 1521. This time-chart shows the dates of the Aztec empire and of some other civilisations that existed in Mexico before then.

STEP BACK IN TIME
At home or at school set up a giant 'time line'. You need:

- a long piece of rope, string or clothes line (about 10 metres)
- some cards or pieces of paper
- pencils and clothes pegs.

Lay the rope on the ground and fix each end so it doesn't move.

You are going to walk back through time in Mexico. Every step is 100 years (a century). Start at one end of the rope and write the present date on a card (it's easier to round it up to AD 2000). Count steps down the rope to the Spanish Conquest and peg on another card with the date. Keep walking and pegging dates until you get back to the beginning of the Olmec period. Try decorating the cards with pictures of the right date, or you could make models.

Be a time detective and find some dates for important events in Mexico after AD 1500 and peg them on your line. You could make another time line for other parts of the world.

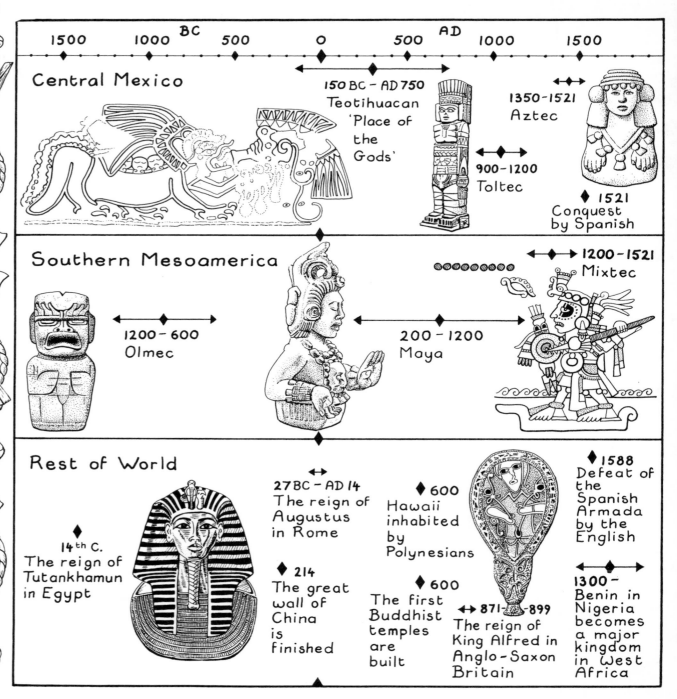

Central Mexico

150 BC – AD 750
Teotihuacan 'Place of the Gods'

1350-1521
Aztec

900-1200
Toltec

1521
Conquest by Spanish

Southern Mesoamerica

1200 – 600
Olmec

200 – 1200
Maya

1200-1521
Mixtec

Rest of World

14th C.
The reign of Tutankhamun in Egypt

27 BC – AD 14
The reign of Augustus in Rome

214
The great wall of China is finished

600
Hawaii inhabited by Polynesians

600
The first Buddhist temples are built

871 – 899
The reign of King Alfred in Anglo-Saxon Britain

1588
Defeat of the Spanish Armada by the English

1300 –
Benin in Nigeria becomes a major kingdom in West Africa

Living on a lake

The Aztecs built their capital city on an island in Lake Texcoco. The city was as large as any city in Europe at the same time. About 250,000 people lived in it. In other books, can you find out what was the population of some cities in Britain in 1500 AD?

The lake provided many things. There were reeds for building, and for making baskets and mats. There was food to eat and trade, like fish, birds, frogs, *axolotl* (a sort of newt), tadpoles, water-flies and their eggs. Dug-out boats carried people and trade goods to the islands and along the many canals in the city. Farmers grew crops such as maize, beans and squash.

As the city grew, they had a clever way to make the islands bigger. To find out what that was, join the dots in the picture.

Merchant game

Merchants – called *pochteca* in the Aztec language, Nahuatl – were a special group with their own laws and customs. They traded goods made in Tenochtitlan (like fine jewellery and cloth) for food, raw cotton, feathers and other riches. They travelled on foot as there were no animals for riding, and porters carried their goods. Many of their trips were very dangerous, often crossing enemy territory. Some journeys took months or years.

In this game you are an Aztec merchant who has travelled hundreds of miles to a distant town. You have to bring your trade goods safely back to Tenochtitlan. Find Tenochtitlan and the four starting-places on the map on page 1.

Jaguar skins
(from Mazatlan)

Spondylus shells
(from Acapulco)

Chillis
(from Tochpan)

Feathers
(from Chiapan)

PLAYING THE GAME

Use coloured counters, or you can trace the drawing of the merchant four times then cut out and colour each one. Trace or draw the bundles of goods four times each and cut them out.

Two to four people can play. Each person chooses a place to start and picks up the goods which come from that place. Take turns to throw a dice and move along the footprints. (In Aztec books, journeys were shown by footprints like these.)

The merchant who gets the most bundles back to Tenochtitlan in the quickest time wins. If you arrive first, you get 4 points, second gets 3, third gets 2, fourth gets 1. Each bundle of goods is worth 1 extra point.

The Aztecs believed their god told them to build their city where they saw an eagle land on a cactus growing out of a rock. The name, Tenochtitlan, comes from *tetl* (rock) and *nochtli* (cactus). Its Aztec name-sign looks like this:

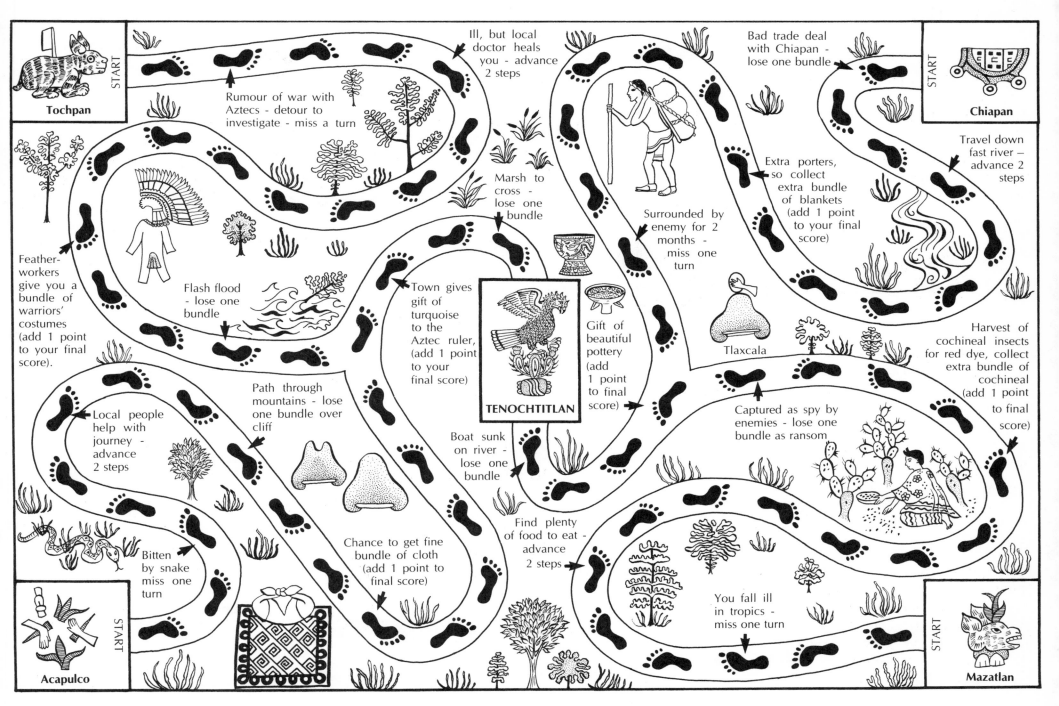

START **Tochpan**

Ill, but local doctor heals you - advance 2 steps

Rumour of war with Aztecs - detour to investigate - miss a turn

Marsh to cross - lose one bundle

Bad trade deal with Chiapan - lose one bundle

START **Chiapan**

Travel down fast river – advance 2 steps

Extra porters, so collect extra bundle of blankets (add 1 point to your final score)

Surrounded by enemy for 2 months - miss one turn

Feather-workers give you a bundle of warriors' costumes (add 1 point to your final score).

Flash flood - lose one bundle

Town gives gift of turquoise to the Aztec ruler, (add 1 point to your final score)

TENOCHTITLAN

Gift of beautiful pottery (add 1 point to final score)

Tlaxcala

Harvest of cochineal insects for red dye, collect extra bundle of cochineal (add 1 point to final score)

Path through mountains - lose one bundle over cliff

Local people help with journey - advance 2 steps

Boat sunk on river - lose one bundle

Captured as spy by enemies - lose one bundle as ransom

Bitten by snake miss one turn

Chance to get fine bundle of cloth (add 1 point to final score)

Find plenty of food to eat - advance 2 steps

You fall ill in tropics - miss one turn

START **Acapulco**

START **Mazatlan**

5

Food and drink

Many foods that we eat every day were first grown by people in Mexico. Here are some: maize, pepper, squash, avocado, tomato, vanilla, chocolate, turkey, chewing gum.

Some of these names come from the Nahuatl language. What are the English names for these words?

....

tomatl   chocolatl   chilli   ahuacatl

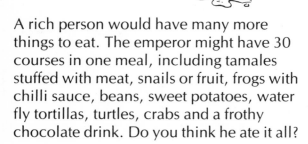

Many women in villages today grind and cook maize in the same way as the Aztecs did. They used a stone roller on a stone base and toasted maize tortillas on a griddle over the fire.

An ordinary Aztec family's menu for a day:

breakfast
maize porridge (*atole*)

spiced with chillis or

sweetened with honey

A rich person would have many more things to eat. The emperor might have 30 courses in one meal, including tamales stuffed with meat, snails or fruit, frogs with chilli sauce, beans, sweet potatoes, water fly tortillas, turtles, crabs and a frothy chocolate drink. Do you think he ate it all?

main meal
tortillas (flat cakes of maize dough)

beans

hot chilli or tomato sauce

tamales (steamed maize dough wrapped in maize husks)

A woman offering frothy chocolate, from a Mixtec book.

Today Mexican food is very popular all over the world. Try this drink – make sure an adult is there to help you.

You need:
100 grams of grated plain chocolate
575 ml (1 pint) milk
1 teaspoon of honey
2 drops of vanilla essence
1 tablespoon of cornflour or maize flour
4 tablespoons of cold water
a sprinkling of powdered cinnamon

To make:

In a saucepan warm the chocolate, milk, sugar and vanilla, stirring all the time. Do not let it boil. Dissolve the cornflour in the water and add slowly to the saucepan, still stirring. Whisk briskly until it bubbles and serve it hot, sprinkled with cinnamon.

What foods would an ancient Aztec recognise in this drink?

Aztec children

Like most Aztec parents, Rain-flower and Eagle-snake's father and mother loved them very much. Aztecs said a baby was like a jewel or a precious flower, and worried about children's health and safety. Aztec parents were very strict, though, punishing children if they did wrong.

In an Aztec book, written about 450 years ago, drawings show some of the jobs children had to do at home. Can you list what they are?

Can you see how old the children are, and how many tortillas they were allowed each day? Remember tortillas are flat cakes. How can you tell that the parents are talking to the children?

Going to school
Commoners' children went to schools called 'Houses of Youth' where boys learned the skills they would need in adult life, like carpentry, fishing, sandal-making or weaving. Many boys trained as warriors. We don't know what girls learned. The children of nobles went to schools run by priests and studied subjects like religion, astronomy, architecture, mathematics and history. The Priests schools made children work very hard. One book called them 'houses of tears'.

Going to market

Rain-flower and Eagle-snake go with their parents to the great city market for the first time. They are amazed at its size. The roads and canals are choked with people and boats bringing items to sell from all over the Aztec world. The family is bringing its harvest of marigolds to sell – they will be used in a fiesta next day.

Can you spot Rain-flower and Eagle-snake in the picture?
Can you identify these people in the market?

- Two chilli sellers arguing over a space
- Porters unloading a boat
- Two children eating tamales at a stall
- Rain-flower and Eagle-snake's parents selling flowers.

Aztecs could tell a lot about each other from their clothes and hairstyles. How many of these people can you identify in the picture?

Commoners: they wore plain garments of brown vegetable fibre (*ixtle*). Men had short hair.

Nobles: they wore fine white cotton, often woven and embroidered with brightly-coloured patterns, with jewellery of jade and gold.

Warriors going to a ceremony: in jaguar or eagle costumes, with their hair in a warrior's lock tied with red cord and feathers. They carried shields decorated with feathers.

9

Games

Life was not all hard work. Music, singing, dancing and poetry were important. Young people learned music and dancing in the House of Song. Aztec musicians had drums, slit-gongs (*teponaztli*) made of wood, rattles and whistles.

A popular board game was patolli. We don't know the exact rules, but players raced their markers around a course painted on a mat. Beans painted with dots were used as dice.

Invent your own version of patolli. You could draw the board on paper or even in sand. Use stones for markers and six dried broad beans, each marked with a dot on one side, for dice. Four people can play. Each person starts and finishes at their 'home'. Decide on rules for when one player lands on another, and what number you need to throw to start and to finish.

The ball-game was a religious event, not just a sport. Two teams tried to keep a rubber ball in the air – they could only hit it with hips, knees and elbows. If one side let the ball drop, the other team scored a point. Sometimes a losing team was sacrificed as an offering to the gods.

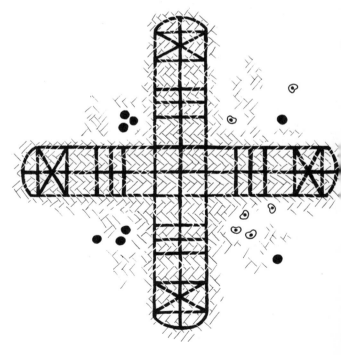

Good days and bad days

The Aztecs had two calendars. One had 365 days. The other had 260 days and was used for ritual. There were 20 day signs and 13 numbers.

Look at the chart. The first day of the 260 day calendar is I alligator, the second day is 2 wind. The fourteenth day is 1 jaguar. Can you see how the numbers and signs repeat? What is the twenty-first day? Fill in the blanks. What would the twenty-eighth day be?

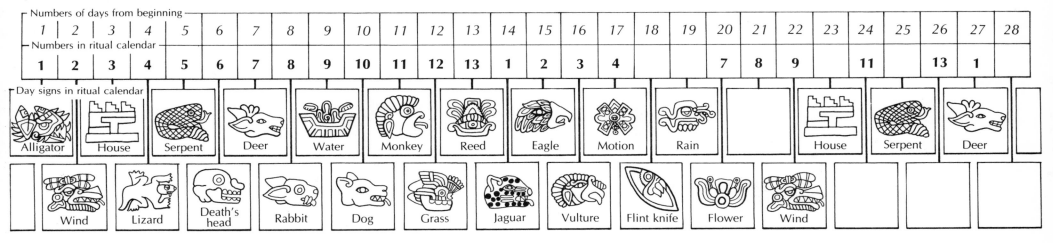

To write day signs like the Aztecs you have to know how they wrote numbers. They counted in 20s (we count in 10s).

 1–19 (dots)

 20 (flag)

 400 (feather)

 8,000 (tasselled bag)

Can you write the numbers 8, 40, 401 in the Aztec style?

The date 7 lizard looks like this:

What would 8 wind look like?

Aztec children had several names. One name was always their birth date, such as One Flower. People thought the day decided the child's future. A child born on 2 rabbit might be a drunkard! Different styles of day names appear in the books of the Aztecs and their neighbours the Mixtecs. What are the names of these two Mixtec people?

Answers: 21st day is 8 Alligator. 28th day is 2 Rabbit.

Gods and goddesses

Aztecs believed in many gods and goddesses who created and controlled the world and kept the sun moving across the sky. To thank the gods and keep them happy, Aztec priests gave them human sacrifices. Slaves or war captives were sacrificed in religious rituals, usually by priests cutting out their hearts.

Aztecs recognised images of their gods by their form, special clothing, ornaments, face decoration and the objects they held. Can you find the items mentioned and redraw them on the 'shelves' next to the gods? Colour them in if you can.

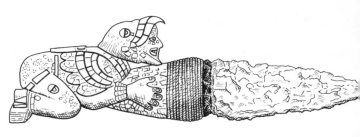

A sacrificial knife. It has a stone blade and a wooden handle in the form of an eagle knight. It is decorated with turquoise and shell.

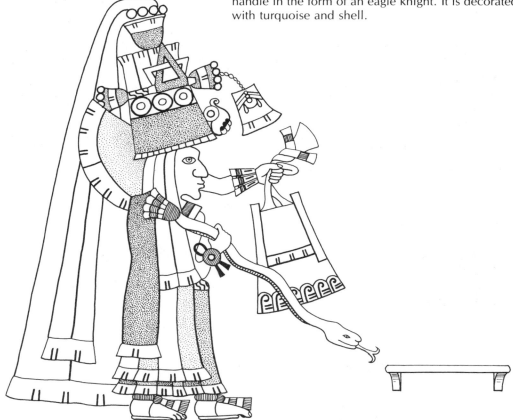

Chalchiuhtlicue

The goddess of the waters. Find her:
Skirt, the colour of water
Green headdress with feathers of the quetzal bird
Round golden pendant

Chicomecoatl

Goddess of ripe maize. Find her:
Rectangle-shaped paper headdress with streamers and tassels
Snake staff

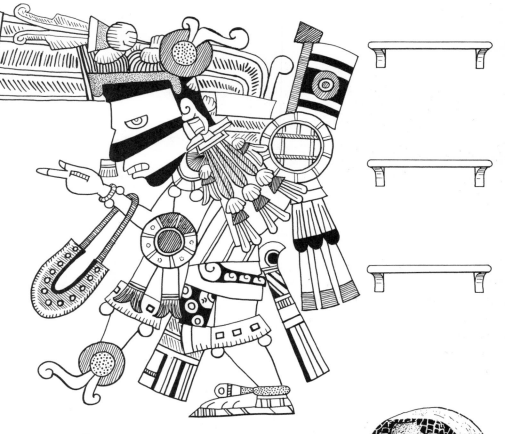

Quetzalcoatl-Ehecatl

Quetzalcoatl means 'Feathered serpent'. Ehecatl means 'wind'. He was the god of learning and crafts and of the wind. Find his:

Jaguar-skin cone-shaped hat
Turquoise ear ornaments
Anklets of jaguar skin with tiny rattles
Large shell-shaped chest ornament
Curved staff
Long beak for the wind god's mouth

Tezcatlipoca

Called 'Smoking mirror', he was the god of warriors, and god of the night sky and of thieves. Find his:
Round mirror of obsidian (a sort of volcanic glass), worn instead of one foot and also on his headdress
Shield
Black striped face paint

This mask in the British Museum represents the god Tezcatlipoca. It is made of a human skull covered with a mosaic of turquoise, black stone and shell.

Books

There were hundreds of thousands of Aztec books, but most were destroyed by the Spaniards after they conquered Mexico. The Spaniards thought books on Aztec religion were evil.

Books were made from animal skin or tree-bark paper. They were folded like this.

One famous book of the Mixtec people tells the story of a leader called Eight Deer.

Aztec writing is different from ours. To 'read' it, a scribe had to understand the meaning of all the details of the pictures – the colours, the numbers, the signs, the costume details. The pictures are called **pictograms**. Some of them represent things:

mountain

house

Some pictograms represent ideas. This one means 'defeat'. It shows a temple on fire with the roof off.

Some also represent words that only *sound* like the thing in the picture

(like for 'I'):

Can you think of some more English examples?

tree (*quauitl*)

teeth (*tlantli*)

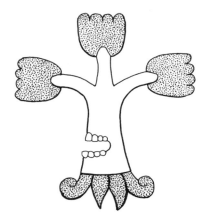

Together they make up the sound of Quauhtitlan (city name)

Can you invent pictograms for some other words?

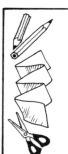

Try making your own Aztec or Mixtec book. You need stiff paper, folded in a zigzag.

Make up a story about your family or friends. Try to write it in coloured pictures in the Aztec way. Think up a sign for each person's name.

The Conquest

In 1519 the Spaniards, led by Hernán Cortés, landed on the shore of Mexico. They fought and defeated the Aztecs and destroyed their city.

These pictures are adapted from Aztec drawings made after the Conquest. Can you match the pictures with the captions below?

1. Aztec nobles greet Cortés on his boat with gifts for a god.

2. Cortés makes allies of other Mexican people. He marches on Tenochtitlan and Emperor Moctezuma meets him.

3. The Spaniards take Moctezuma captive. He shows them his treasure house.

4. At an Aztec festival, the Spaniards attack the crowd and kill many people.

5. The Aztecs fight. Moctezuma is killed.

6. The Aztecs attack the Spaniards and their allies who are escaping across a causeway. The Aztecs attack from the water.

7. Aztecs catch smallpox from the Spaniards and many die.

8. The Spaniards attack again and finally the Aztecs are defeated.

This is a Aztec poem written after the Spanish Conquest:

Broken spears lie in the roads
we have torn our hair in our grief
the houses are roofless now, and their
walls are red with blood.

Try writing your own poem about the Aztecs.

Aztecs today

The descendants of the Aztecs still live in Mexico today, along with many other native groups. Most Mexicans have both native and European ancestors, and the main language is Spanish.

Festivals are an important part of Mexican life. The Day of the Dead is celebrated at the beginning of November. Mexicans believe that the souls of the dead visit their living relatives then. It is a happy time, and families prepare an *ofrenda* (a table of food and decorations) for the souls. It is a Christian festival, but some of the food, decorations and customs are the same as in Aztec times.

How many things can you identify in this picture of an *ofrenda*? Look for special bread in odd shapes, a container for burning incense, marigolds, steamed tamales hung up as decorations and other decorations made of strips of palm leaves.

© 1994 The Trustees of the British Museum

Published by British Museum Press
A division of British Museum Publications Ltd
46 Bloomsbury Street, London WC1B 3QQ

ISBN 0-7141-2514-8

Drawings and back cover illustration: Patricia Hansom
Front cover illustration: Peter Dennis

Typeset by Rowland Phototypesetting Limited, Bury St Edmunds, Suffolk
and printed by St Edmundsbury Press Limited, Bury St Edmunds, Suffolk